EASY PIANO

BROADWAY SHEET MUSIC HITS

Arranged by DAN COATES

C000138105

Published 2004

© International Music Publications Ltd
Griffin House 161 Hammersmith Road London W6 8BS England

Editorial management: Artemis Music Limited (www.artemismusic.com)

Almost Like Being In Love
(from *Brigadoon*)

Words by Alan Jay Lerner
Music by Frederick Loewe

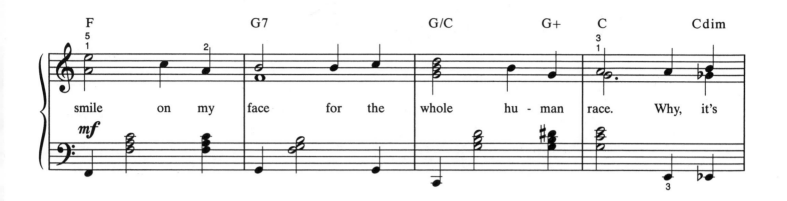

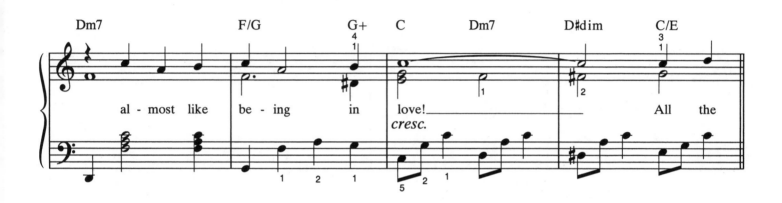

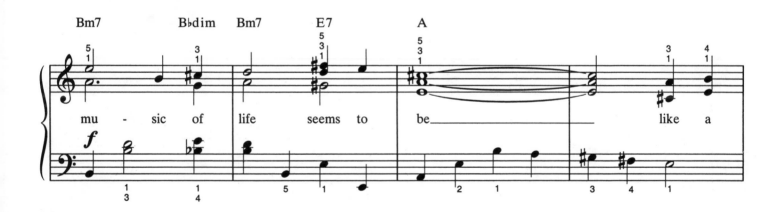

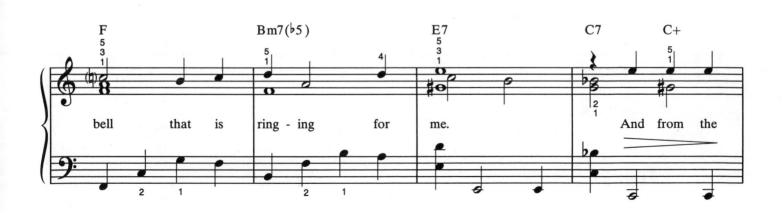

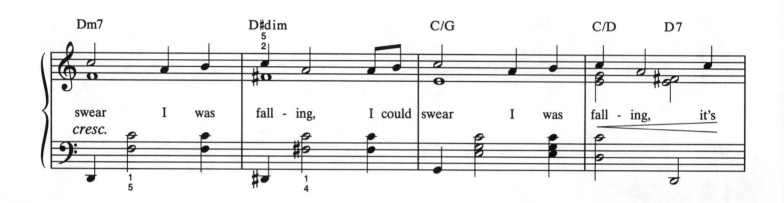

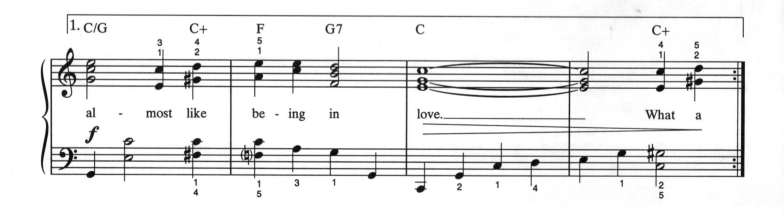

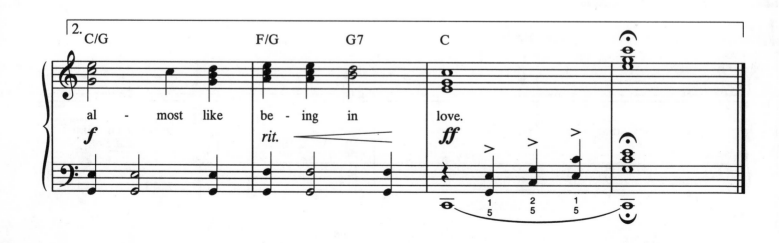

And All That Jazz
(from *Chicago*)

Words by John Kander
Music by Fred Ebb

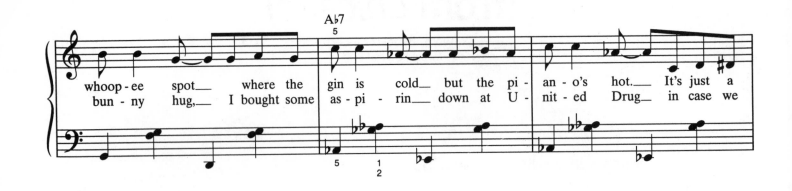

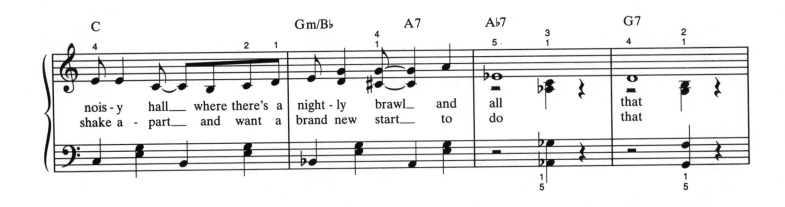

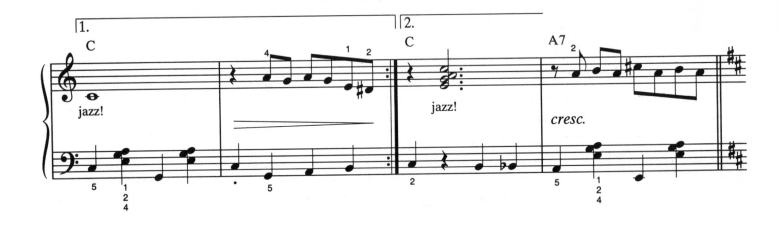

all that   jazz!__)   Oh,   she' gon - na shim-my 'til her

gar - ters   break.__   (And   all   that   jazz!__)   Show__

__ her where to park her gir-dle,   oh,__   her moth-er's blood-'d cur-dle

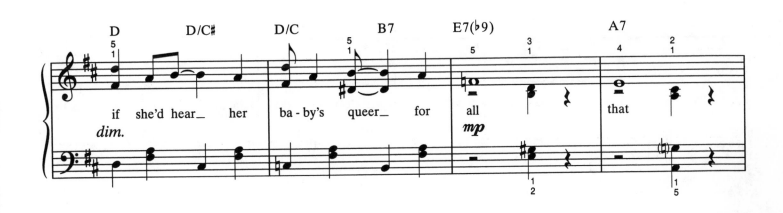

if she'd hear__ her   ba - by's   queer__ for   all   that

Beautiful City
(from *Godspell*)

Words and Music by Stephen Schwartz

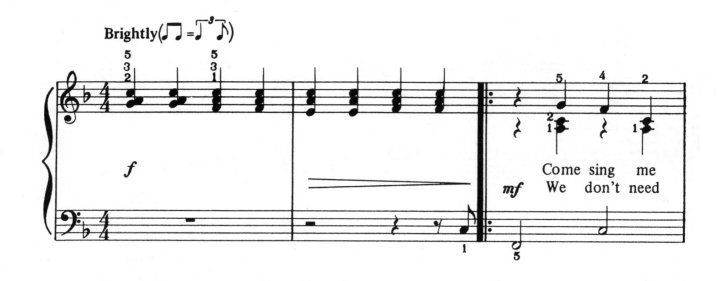

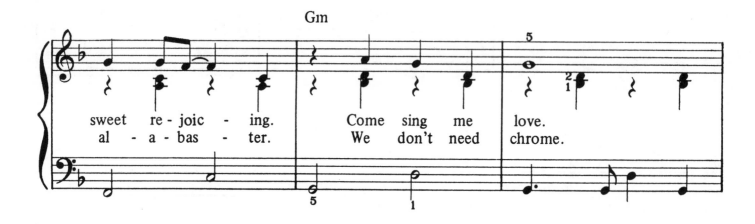

Bewitched
(from *Pal Joey*)

Words by Lorenz Hart
Music by Richard Rodgers

Favourite Son
(from *The Will Rodgers Follies*)

Words by Betty Comden and Adolph Green
Music by Cy Coleman

Famous Music Publishing Ltd, London SW6 3JW

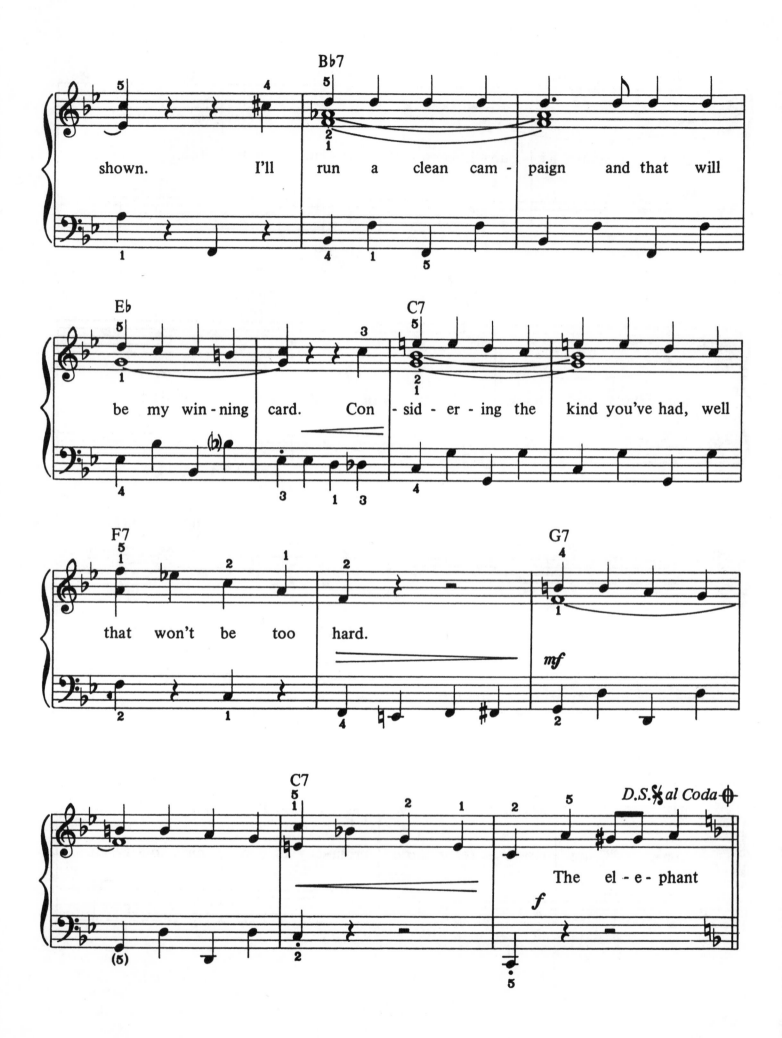

Cabaret
(from *Cabaret*)

Words by Fred Ebb
Music by John Kander

Dancing Queen
(from *Mamma Mia*)

Words and Music by Benny Andersson, Bjoern Ulvaeus and Stig Anderson

Evergreen
(from *A Star Is Born*)

Words by Paul Williams
Music by Barbra Streisand

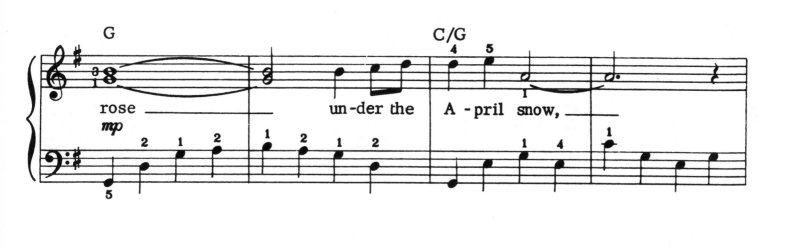

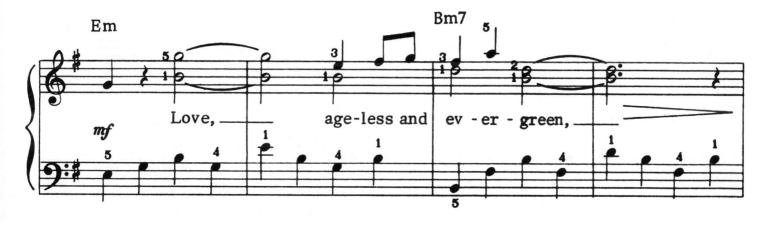

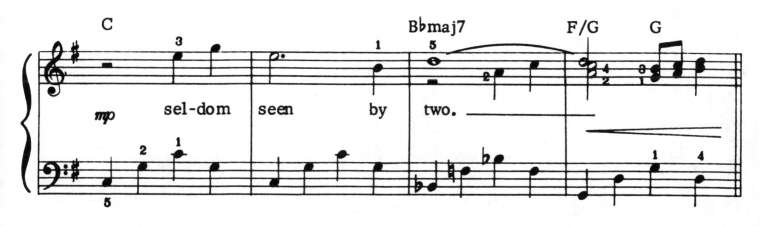

Falling In Love With Love
(from *The Boys From Syracuse*)

Words by Lorenz Hart
Music by Richard Rodgers

Moderate Waltz

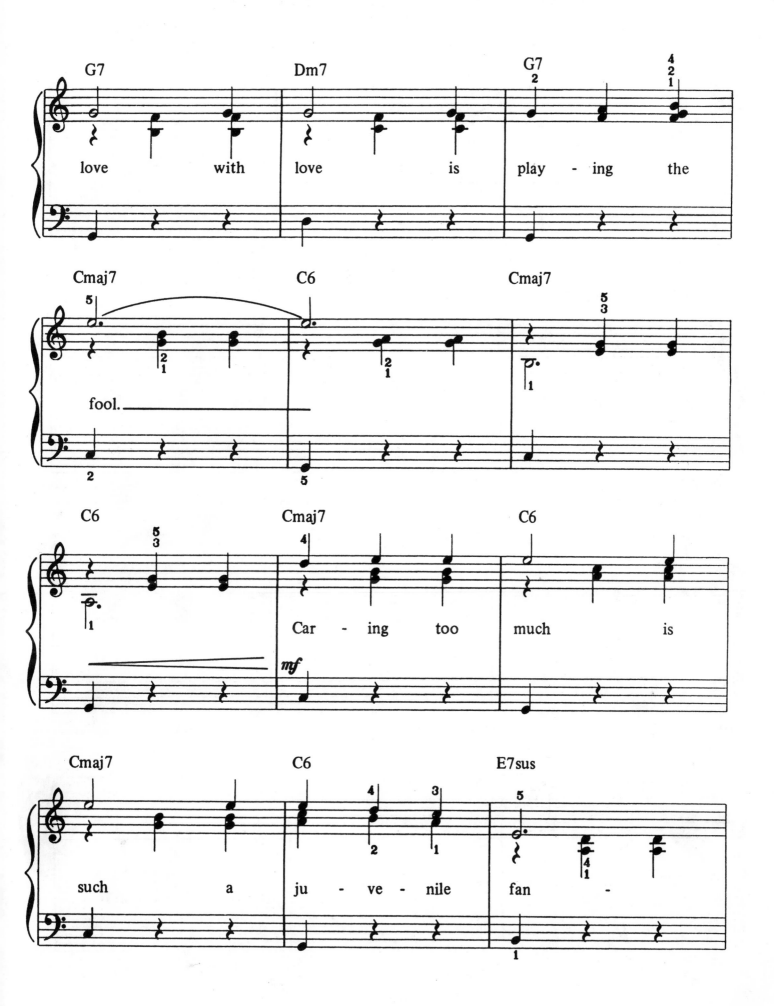

Forty Second Street
(from *Forty Second Street*)

Words by Al Dubin
Music by Harry Warren

Moderately fast

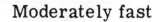

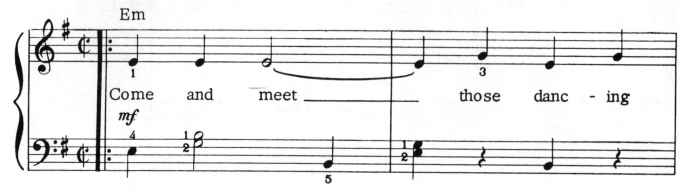

Come and meet those danc - ing

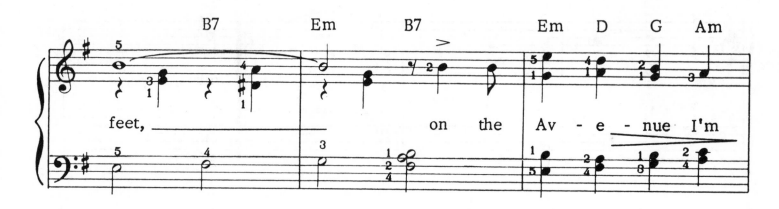

feet, _____ on the Av - e - nue I'm

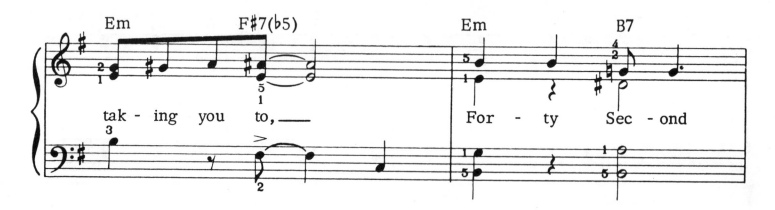

tak - ing you to, ___ For - ty Sec - ond

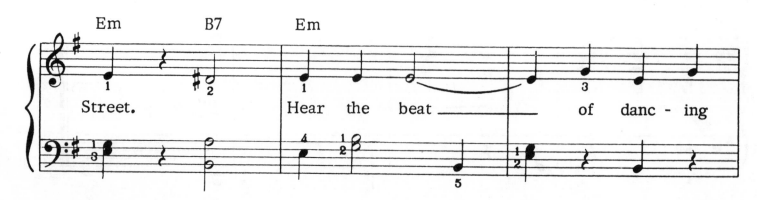

Street. Hear the beat _____ of danc - ing

feet, _____ it's the song I love the

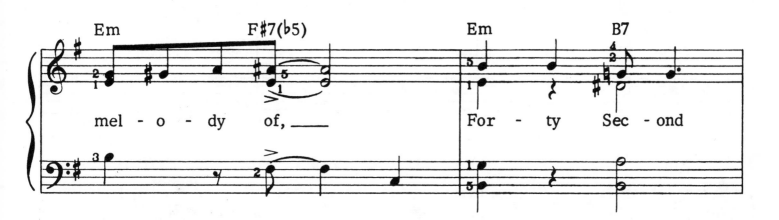

mel - o - dy of, _____ For - ty Sec - ond

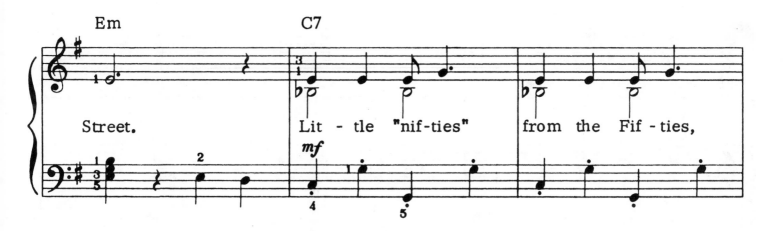

Street. Lit - tle "nif-ties" from the Fif - ties,

in - no - cent and sweet' sex - y la-dies

Heart
(from *Damn Yankees*)

Words and Music by Richard Adler and Jerry Ross

Hey There
(from *The Pajama Game*)

Words and Music by Richard Adler and Jerry Ross

Moderately slow, with expression

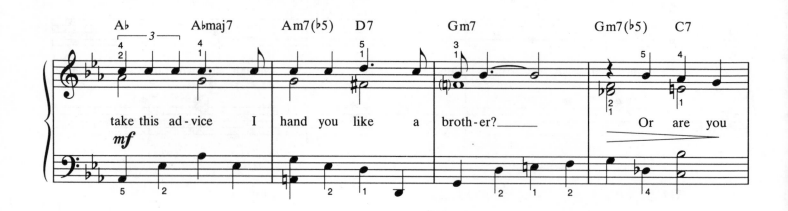

take this ad-vice I hand you like a broth-er?_____ Or are you

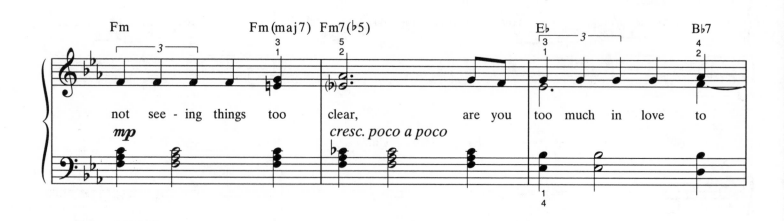

not see-ing things too clear, are you too much in love to

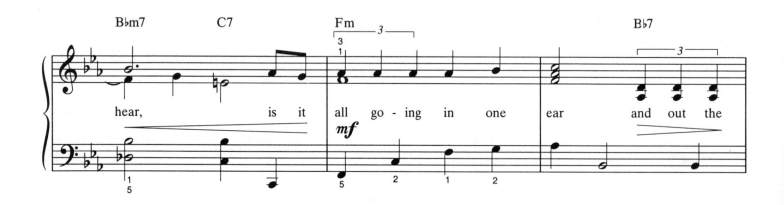

hear, is it all go-ing in one ear and out the

oth - er? oth - er?

If I Were A Rich Man
(from *Fiddler On The Roof*)

Words by Sheldon Harnick
Music by Jerry Bock

How Could I Ever Know?
(from *The Secret Garden*)

Words by Marsha Norman
Music by Lucy Simon

My Funny Valentine
(from *Babes In Arms*)

Words by Lorenz Hart
Music by Richard Rodgers

Slowly, with much expression

mp legato

Cm   G/C   Cm7

My fun - ny Val - en - tine, sweet com - ic

Dm7/C   Ab   Fm

Val - en - tine, you make me smile with my

Dm7(b5)   G7   Cm   G7/C

heart._____ Your looks are laugh - a - ble,

Over The Rainbow
(from *The Wizard Of Oz*)

Words by E Y Harburg
Music by Harold Arlen

Ragtime
(from *Ragtime*)

Words by Lynn Ahrens
Music by Stephen Flaherty

Moderato (Not too quick)

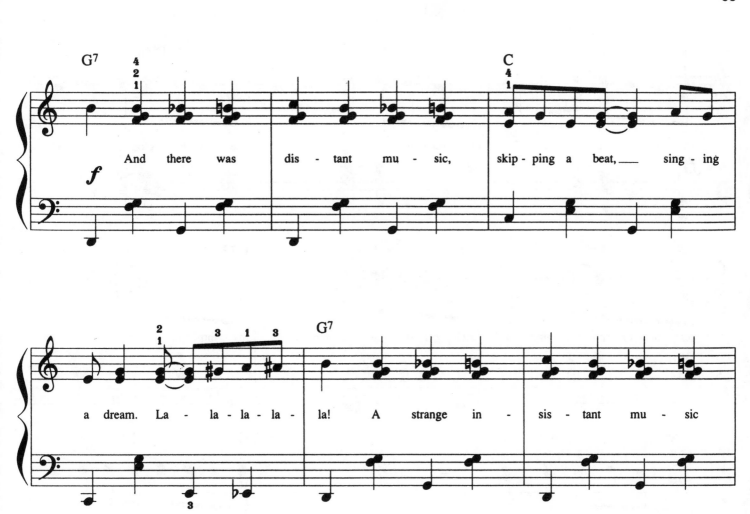

And there was dis - tant mu - sic, skip - ping a beat, ___ sing - ing

a dream. La - la - la - la - la! A strange in - sis - tant mu - sic

put - ting out heat, ___ pick - ing up steam. La - la - la - la - la! The sound of

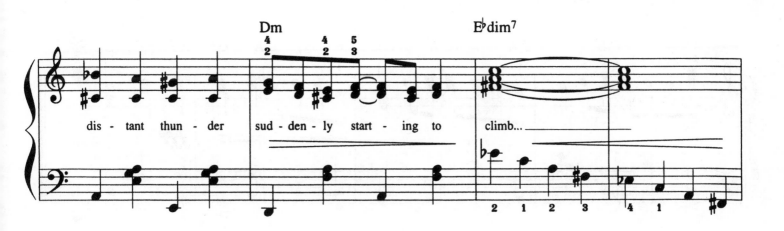

dis - tant thun - der sud - den - ly start - ing to climb...

What More Can I Say?
(from *Falsettos*)

Words and Music by William Finn

Moderate Ballad

(Pedal throughout)

It's been hot, al-so ver-y sweet. And I'm not u-su-al-ly in-dis-creet, but when he spar-kles, the earth be-gins to sway. What more can I

Send In The Clowns
(from *A Little Night Music*)

Words and Music by Stephen Sondheim

Slowly, with expression

Summertime
(from *Porgy And Bess*®)

Music and Lyrics by George Gershwin, Du Bose Heyward, Dorothy Heyward and Ira Gershwin

Moderately, with expression

Sunrise, Sunset
(from *Fiddler On The Roof*)

Words by Sheldon Harnick
Music by Jerry Bock

2. Now is the little boy a bridegroom,
   Now is the little girl a bride.
   Under a canopy I see them, side by side.
   Place the gold ring around her finger,
   Share the sweet wine and break the glass;
   Soon the full circle will have come to pass.
   (To Chorus:)

Tenterfield Saddler
(from *The Boy From Oz*)

Words and Music by Peter Allen

Moderately slow

1. The late George Wool - nough worked on High Street and
son of George Wool - nough went off and got mar - ried, and

lived on man - ners. Fif - ty - two years he
had a war ba - by. Though some - thing was wrong and it's

sat on his ver - an - dah and made his sad - dles. And
eas - i - er to drink than and go cra - zy. And

if you had ques - tions 'bout sheep ____ or flow - ers or
if there were ques - tions 'bout why ____ the end was so

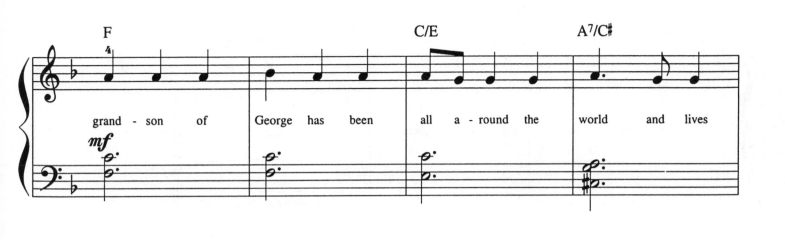

grand - son of George has been all a - round the world and lives

no spe - cial place,

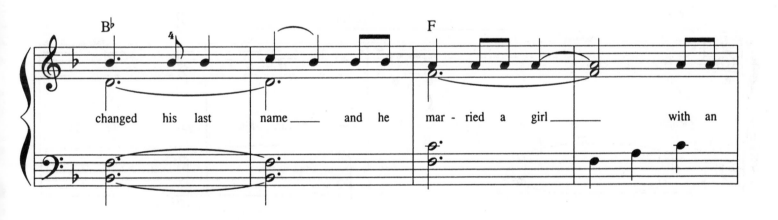

changed his last name____ and he mar - ried a girl____ with an

in - t'rest - ing face. He'd

With A Song In My Heart
(from *Spring Is Here*)

Words by Lorenz Hart
Music by Richard Rodgers

Moderately Slow, steady rhythm

You Can Always Count On Me
(from *City Of Angels*)

Words by David Zippel
Music by Cy Coleman

Extra Lyrics:

3. Though my kind of dame no doubt will die out
Like the dinosaurs,
You can always count on me.
I'm solely to blame, my head gives advice
That my heart ignores.
I'm my only enemy.
I choose the kind who cannot introduce
The girl he's with;
They're lots of smirking motel clerks
Who call me Missus Smith.
But I've made a name with hotel detectives
Who break down doors.
Guess who they expect to see? (etc...)

You Took Advantage Of Me
(from *Present Arms*)

Words by Lorenz Hart
Music by Richard Rodgers

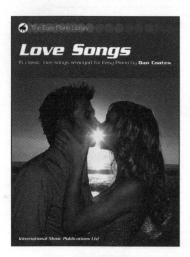 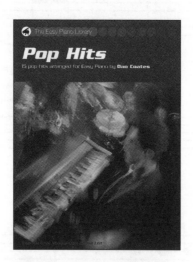  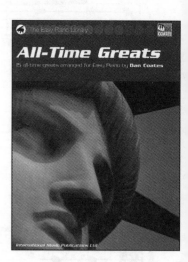

LOVE SONGS
9544A   E/PNO   ISBN: 1-84328-115-5

Angel Of Mine - Because You Loved Me - Get Here - The Greatest Love Of All - Have I Told You Lately That I Love You - I'd Lie For You (And That's The Truth) - I Turn To You - Now And Forever - The Prayer - Right Here Waiting - The Rose - Something About The Way You Look Tonight - Unbreak My Heart - When You Tell Me That You Love Me - 2 Become 1

POP HITS
9546A   E/PNO   ISBN: 1-84328-117-1

Amazed - Believe - Can't Fight The Moonlight - Genie In A Bottle - Heal The World - How Do I Live - I'll Be There For You - Kiss The Rain - Livin' La Vida Loca - Macarena - Music - Quit Playing Games With My Heart - Smooth - Swear It Again - Thank You

FILM FAVOURITES
9545A   E/PNO   ISBN: 1-84328-116-3

Batman Theme - Beautiful Stranger - Because You Loved Me - Can You Feel The Love Tonight - Can't Fight The Moonlight - Evergreen - (Everything I Do) I Do It For You - I Don't Want To Miss A Thing - Imperial March (Darth Vader's Theme) - I Will Always Love You - Somewhere My Love (Lara's Theme) - Star Wars (Main Theme) - Superman Theme - Wind Beneath My Wings

ALL TIME GREATS
9603A   E/PNO   ISBN: 1-84328-138-4

American Pie – As Time Goes By – Desperado – The Greatest Love Of All – Hotel California – Lean On Me – My Heart Will Go On – My Way – Over The Rainbow – Sacrifice – Save The Best For Last – Send In The Clowns – Stairway To Heaven – Theme From New York, New York – When You Tell Me That You Love Me

GREAT SONGWRITERS
9671A   E/PNO   ISBN: 1-84328-175-3

As Time Goes By – Bewitched – Cabaret – High Hopes – I Got Plenty O' Nuttin' – It Ain't Necessarily So – Love & Marriage – Maybe This Time – Never Met A Man I Din't Like – Over The Rainbow – Raindrops Keep Fallin' On My Head – Send In The Clowns – Singin' In The Rain – Summertime – Tomorrow

CHRISTMAS SONGS
9790A   E/PNO   ISBN: 1-84328-309-3

All I Want For Christmas Is My Two Front Teeth - Deck The Hall - It's The Most Wonderful Time Of The Year - Jingle Bells - Let it Snow! Let it Snow! Let it Snow! - The Little Drummer Boy - Little Saint Nick - Have Yourself A Merry Little Christmas - I Believe In Santa Claus - The Most Wonderful Day Of The Year - O Christmas Tree - Rockin' Around The Christmas Tree - Rudolph, The Red-Nosed Reindeer - Santa Claus Is Comin' To Town - Sleigh Ride - The Twelve Days Of Christmas - Winter Wonderland